MW00799353

You do not just have one story to tell.

You have endless stories inside of you, just waiting to be told.

The goal of this workbook is to help you be able to spot storytelling opportunities at any given time and to know which story will be the most effective to use.

But in order to do that, you need to make it a consistent practice. And in order to do that, you must first understand the structure that every great story is founded upon.

In each story, you will need to establish the Four P's:

PEOPLE: Who is my story about?
PROBLEM: What are they struggling with?
PURPOSE: Why am I telling this story?
PLATFORM: When and where will I share this story?

It's a simple structure that breaks down the essential elements of a great story.

These exercises will allow you to work that storytelling muscle on a daily or weekly basis.

And soon, you will be well on your way to becoming a compelling storyteller!

DATE:

PEOPLE

- Who is the character or characters? _____

- Where are they in their lives? _____

- What are they struggling with? _____

- What is their flawed belief about the world or themselves? _____

PROBLEM

- What happens that creates a new problem for them? _____

- Who or what comes along to help them? _____

- How do they finally accomplish their goal? _____

- How do they change as a result? _____

STORY TITLE:

PURPOSE

- Who are you telling this story to? _____

_____

_____

_____

- What is the emotion you want them to feel? _____

_____

_____

_____

- What is the message you want them to receive? _____

_____

_____

_____

- What action do you want your audience to take? _____

_____

_____

_____

PLATFORM

- What format will you use to tell this story? _____

_____

_____

_____

- On which platform will you distribute it? _____

_____

_____

_____

- How can you creatively repurpose it? _____

_____

_____

_____

- How will you measure its success? _____

_____

_____

_____

PEOPLE

- Who is the character or characters? _____

- Where are they in their lives? _____

- What are they struggling with? _____

- What is their flawed belief about the world or themselves? _____

PROBLEM

- What happens that creates a new problem for them? _____

- Who or what comes along to help them? _____

- How do they finally accomplish their goal? _____

- How do they change as a result? _____

STORY TITLE:

PURPOSE

- Who are you telling this story to? _____
_____
_____

- What is the emotion you want them to feel? _____
_____
_____

- What is the message you want them to receive? _____
_____
_____

- What action do you want your audience to take? _____
_____
_____

PLATFORM

- What format will you use to tell this story? _____
_____
_____

- On which platform will you distribute it? _____
_____
_____

- How can you creatively repurpose it? _____
_____
_____

- How will you measure its success? _____
_____
_____

DATE:

PEOPLE

- Who is the character or characters? _____
  _____
  _____
  _____

- Where are they in their lives? _____
  _____
  _____
  _____

- What are they struggling with? _____
  _____
  _____
  _____

- What is their flawed belief about the world or themselves? _____
  _____
  _____
  _____

PROBLEM

- What happens that creates a new problem for them? _____
  _____
  _____
  _____

- Who or what comes along to help them? _____
  _____
  _____
  _____

- How do they finally accomplish their goal? _____
  _____
  _____
  _____

- How do they change as a result? _____
  _____
  _____
  _____

STORY TITLE:

PURPOSE

- Who are you telling this story to? _____
  _____
  _____

- What is the emotion you want them to feel? _____
  _____
  _____

- What is the message you want them to receive? _____
  _____
  _____

- What action do you want your audience to take? _____
  _____
  _____

PLATFORM

- What format will you use to tell this story? _____
  _____
  _____

- On which platform will you distribute it? _____
  _____
  _____

- How can you creatively repurpose it? _____
  _____
  _____

- How will you measure its success? _____
  _____
  _____

PEOPLE

- Who is the character or characters? _____
  _____
  _____
  _____

- Where are they in their lives? _____
  _____
  _____
  _____

- What are they struggling with? _____
  _____
  _____
  _____

- What is their flawed belief about the world or themselves? _____
  _____
  _____
  _____

PROBLEM

- What happens that creates a new problem for them? _____
  _____
  _____
  _____

- Who or what comes along to help them? _____
  _____
  _____
  _____

- How do they finally accomplish their goal? _____
  _____
  _____

- How do they change as a result? _____
  _____
  _____
  _____

STORY TITLE:

PURPOSE

- Who are you telling this story to? _____

_____

- What is the emotion you want them to feel? _____

_____

- What is the message you want them to receive? _____

_____

- What action do you want your audience to take? _____

_____

PLATFORM

- What format will you use to tell this story? _____

_____

- On which platform will you distribute it? _____

_____

- How can you creatively repurpose it? _____

_____

- How will you measure its success? _____

_____

DATE:

PEOPLE

- Who is the character or characters? _____

- Where are they in their lives? _____

- What are they struggling with? _____

- What is their flawed belief about the world or themselves? _____

PROBLEM

- What happens that creates a new problem for them? _____

- Who or what comes along to help them? _____

- How do they finally accomplish their goal? _____

- How do they change as a result? _____

STORY TITLE:

PURPOSE

- Who are you telling this story to? _____
  _____
  _____
  _____

- What is the emotion you want them to feel? _____
  _____
  _____
  _____

- What is the message you want them to receive? _____
  _____
  _____
  _____

- What action do you want your audience to take? _____
  _____
  _____
  _____

PLATFORM

- What format will you use to tell this story? _____
  _____
  _____
  _____

- On which platform will you distribute it? _____
  _____
  _____
  _____

- How can you creatively repurpose it? _____
  _____
  _____
  _____

- How will you measure its success? _____
  _____
  _____
  _____

PEOPLE

- Who is the character or characters? _____

- Where are they in their lives? _____

- What are they struggling with? _____

- What is their flawed belief about the world or themselves? _____

PROBLEM

- What happens that creates a new problem for them? _____

- Who or what comes along to help them? _____

- How do they finally accomplish their goal? _____

- How do they change as a result? _____

STORY TITLE:

PURPOSE

- Who are you telling this story to? _____

_____

_____

- What is the emotion you want them to feel? _____

_____

_____

- What is the message you want them to receive? _____

_____

_____

- What action do you want your audience to take? _____

_____

_____

PLATFORM

- What format will you use to tell this story? _____

_____

_____

- On which platform will you distribute it? _____

_____

_____

- How can you creatively repurpose it? _____

_____

_____

- How will you measure its success? _____

_____

_____

DATE:

PEOPLE

- Who is the character or characters? _____
  _____
  _____
  _____

- Where are they in their lives? _____
  _____
  _____
  _____

- What are they struggling with? _____
  _____
  _____
  _____

- What is their flawed belief about the world or themselves? _____
  _____
  _____
  _____

PROBLEM

- What happens that creates a new problem for them? _____
  _____
  _____
  _____

- Who or what comes along to help them? _____
  _____
  _____
  _____

- How do they finally accomplish their goal? _____
  _____
  _____
  _____

- How do they change as a result? _____
  _____
  _____

STORY TITLE:

PURPOSE

- Who are you telling this story to? _____
_____
_____

- What is the emotion you want them to feel? _____
_____
_____

- What is the message you want them to receive? _____
_____
_____

- What action do you want your audience to take? _____
_____
_____

PLATFORM

- What format will you use to tell this story? _____
_____
_____

- On which platform will you distribute it? _____
_____
_____

- How can you creatively repurpose it? _____
_____
_____

- How will you measure its success? _____
_____
_____

DATE:

PEOPLE

- Who is the character or characters? _____
_____
_____

- Where are they in their lives? _____
_____
_____

- What are they struggling with? _____
_____
_____

- What is their flawed belief about the world or themselves? _____
_____
_____

PROBLEM

- What happens that creates a new problem for them? _____
_____
_____

- Who or what comes along to help them? _____
_____
_____

- How do they finally accomplish their goal? _____
_____
_____

- How do they change as a result? _____
_____
_____

STORY TITLE:

PURPOSE

- Who are you telling this story to? _____
_____
_____
_____

- What is the emotion you want them to feel? _____
_____
_____
_____

- What is the message you want them to receive? _____
_____
_____
_____

- What action do you want your audience to take? _____
_____
_____
_____

PLATFORM

- What format will you use to tell this story? _____
_____
_____
_____

- On which platform will you distribute it? _____
_____
_____
_____

- How can you creatively repurpose it? _____
_____
_____
_____

- How will you measure its success? _____
_____
_____
_____

PEOPLE

- Who is the character or characters? _____
  _____
  _____
  _____

- Where are they in their lives? _____
  _____
  _____
  _____

- What are they struggling with? _____
  _____
  _____
  _____

- What is their flawed belief about the world or themselves? _____
  _____
  _____
  _____

PROBLEM

- What happens that creates a new problem for them? _____
  _____
  _____
  _____

- Who or what comes along to help them? _____
  _____
  _____
  _____

- How do they finally accomplish their goal? _____
  _____
  _____
  _____

- How do they change as a result? _____
  _____
  _____
  _____

STORY TITLE:

PURPOSE

- Who are you telling this story to? _____
_____
_____

- What is the emotion you want them to feel? _____
_____
_____

- What is the message you want them to receive? _____
_____
_____

- What action do you want your audience to take? _____
_____
_____

PLATFORM

- What format will you use to tell this story? _____
_____
_____

- On which platform will you distribute it? _____
_____
_____

- How can you creatively repurpose it? _____
_____
_____

- How will you measure its success? _____
_____
_____

PEOPLE

- Who is the character or characters? _____
  _____
  _____
  _____

- Where are they in their lives? _____
  _____
  _____
  _____

- What are they struggling with? _____
  _____
  _____
  _____

- What is their flawed belief about the world or themselves? _____
  _____
  _____
  _____

PROBLEM

- What happens that creates a new problem for them? _____
  _____
  _____
  _____

- Who or what comes along to help them? _____
  _____
  _____
  _____

- How do they finally accomplish their goal? _____
  _____
  _____
  _____

- How do they change as a result? _____
  _____
  _____
  _____

STORY TITLE:

PURPOSE

- Who are you telling this story to? _____
_____
_____
_____

- What is the emotion you want them to feel? _____
_____
_____
_____

- What is the message you want them to receive? _____
_____
_____
_____

- What action do you want your audience to take? _____
_____
_____
_____

PLATFORM

- What format will you use to tell this story? _____
_____
_____
_____

- On which platform will you distribute it? _____
_____
_____
_____

- How can you creatively repurpose it? _____
_____
_____
_____

- How will you measure its success? _____
_____
_____
_____

DATE:

PEOPLE

- Who is the character or characters? _____
  _____
  _____
  _____

- Where are they in their lives? _____
  _____
  _____
  _____

- What are they struggling with? _____
  _____
  _____
  _____

- What is their flawed belief about the world or themselves? _____
  _____
  _____
  _____

PROBLEM

- What happens that creates a new problem for them? _____
  _____
  _____
  _____

- Who or what comes along to help them? _____
  _____
  _____
  _____

- How do they finally accomplish their goal? _____
  _____
  _____
  _____

- How do they change as a result? _____
  _____
  _____

STORY TITLE:

PURPOSE

- Who are you telling this story to? _____
_____
_____
_____

- What is the emotion you want them to feel? _____
_____
_____
_____

- What is the message you want them to receive? _____
_____
_____
_____

- What action do you want your audience to take? _____
_____
_____
_____

PLATFORM

- What format will you use to tell this story? _____
_____
_____
_____

- On which platform will you distribute it? _____
_____
_____
_____

- How can you creatively repurpose it? _____
_____
_____
_____

- How will you measure its success? _____
_____
_____
_____

DATE:

PEOPLE

- Who is the character or characters? _____
  _____
  _____

- Where are they in their lives? _____
  _____
  _____

- What are they struggling with? _____
  _____
  _____

- What is their flawed belief about the world or themselves? _____
  _____
  _____

PROBLEM

- What happens that creates a new problem for them? _____
  _____
  _____

- Who or what comes along to help them? _____
  _____
  _____

- How do they finally accomplish their goal? _____
  _____
  _____

- How do they change as a result? _____
  _____
  _____

STORY TITLE:

PURPOSE

- Who are you telling this story to? _____
  _____
  _____
  _____

- What is the emotion you want them to feel? _____
  _____
  _____
  _____

- What is the message you want them to receive? _____
  _____
  _____
  _____

- What action do you want your audience to take? _____
  _____
  _____
  _____

PLATFORM

- What format will you use to tell this story? _____
  _____
  _____
  _____

- On which platform will you distribute it? _____
  _____
  _____
  _____

- How can you creatively repurpose it? _____
  _____
  _____
  _____

How will you measure its success? _____
  _____
  _____
  _____

PEOPLE

- Who is the character or characters? _____
  _____
  _____
  _____

- Where are they in their lives? _____
  _____
  _____
  _____

- What are they struggling with? _____
  _____
  _____
  _____

- What is their flawed belief about the world or themselves? _____
  _____
  _____
  _____

PROBLEM

- What happens that creates a new problem for them? _____
  _____
  _____
  _____

- Who or what comes along to help them? _____
  _____
  _____
  _____

- How do they finally accomplish their goal? _____
  _____
  _____
  _____

- How do they change as a result? _____
  _____
  _____
  _____

PURPOSE

- Who are you telling this story to? _____

- What is the emotion you want them to feel? _____

- What is the message you want them to receive? _____

- What action do you want your audience to take? _____

PLATFORM

- What format will you use to tell this story? _____

- On which platform will you distribute it? _____

- How can you creatively repurpose it? _____

- How will you measure its success? _____

PEOPLE

- Who is the character or characters? _____
  _____
  _____
  _____

- Where are they in their lives? _____
  _____
  _____
  _____

- What are they struggling with? _____
  _____
  _____

- What is their flawed belief about the world or themselves? _____
  _____
  _____
  _____

PROBLEM

- What happens that creates a new problem for them? _____
  _____
  _____
  _____

- Who or what comes along to help them? _____
  _____
  _____
  _____

- How do they finally accomplish their goal? _____
  _____
  _____
  _____

- How do they change as a result? _____
  _____
  _____
  _____

STORY TITLE:

PURPOSE

- Who are you telling this story to? _____
_____
_____
_____

- What is the emotion you want them to feel? _____
_____
_____
_____

- What is the message you want them to receive? _____
_____
_____
_____

- What action do you want your audience to take? _____
_____
_____
_____

PLATFORM

- What format will you use to tell this story? _____
_____
_____
_____

- On which platform will you distribute it? _____
_____
_____
_____

- How can you creatively repurpose it? _____
_____
_____
_____

- How will you measure its success? _____
_____
_____
_____

PEOPLE

- Who is the character or characters? _____
  _____
  _____
  _____

- Where are they in their lives? _____
  _____
  _____
  _____

- What are they struggling with? _____
  _____
  _____
  _____

- What is their flawed belief about the world or themselves? _____
  _____
  _____
  _____

PROBLEM

- What happens that creates a new problem for them? _____
  _____
  _____
  _____

- Who or what comes along to help them? _____
  _____
  _____
  _____

- How do they finally accomplish their goal? _____
  _____
  _____
  _____

- How do they change as a result? _____
  _____
  _____
  _____

STORY TITLE:

PURPOSE

- Who are you telling this story to? _____

_____

_____

- What is the emotion you want them to feel? _____

_____

_____

- What is the message you want them to receive? _____

_____

_____

- What action do you want your audience to take? _____

_____

_____

PLATFORM

- What format will you use to tell this story? _____

_____

_____

- On which platform will you distribute it? _____

_____

_____

- How can you creatively repurpose it? _____

_____

_____

- How will you measure its success? _____

_____

_____

PEOPLE

- Who is the character or characters? _____

_____

_____

_____

- Where are they in their lives? _____

_____

_____

_____

- What are they struggling with? _____

_____

_____

_____

- What is their flawed belief about the world or themselves? _____

_____

_____

_____

PROBLEM

- What happens that creates a new problem for them? _____

_____

_____

_____

- Who or what comes along to help them? _____

_____

_____

_____

- How do they finally accomplish their goal? _____

_____

_____

_____

- How do they change as a result? _____

_____

_____

_____

STORY TITLE:

PURPOSE

- Who are you telling this story to? _____
_____
_____
_____

- What is the emotion you want them to feel? _____
_____
_____
_____

- What is the message you want them to receive? _____
_____
_____
_____

- What action do you want your audience to take? _____
_____
_____
_____

PLATFORM

- What format will you use to tell this story? _____
_____
_____
_____

- On which platform will you distribute it? _____
_____
_____
_____

- How can you creatively repurpose it? _____
_____
_____
_____

- How will you measure its success? _____
_____
_____
_____

PEOPLE

- Who is the character or characters? _____
  _____
  _____

- Where are they in their lives? _____
  _____
  _____

- What are they struggling with? _____
  _____
  _____

- What is their flawed belief about the world or themselves? _____
  _____
  _____
  _____

PROBLEM

- What happens that creates a new problem for them? _____
  _____
  _____
  _____

- Who or what comes along to help them? _____
  _____
  _____
  _____

- How do they finally accomplish their goal? _____
  _____
  _____
  _____

- How do they change as a result? _____
  _____
  _____
  _____

STORY TITLE:

PURPOSE

- Who are you telling this story to? _____
  _____
  _____
  _____

- What is the emotion you want them to feel? _____
  _____
  _____
  _____

- What is the message you want them to receive? _____
  _____
  _____
  _____

- What action do you want your audience to take? _____
  _____
  _____
  _____

PLATFORM

- What format will you use to tell this story? _____
  _____
  _____
  _____

- On which platform will you distribute it? _____
  _____
  _____
  _____

- How can you creatively repurpose it? _____
  _____
  _____

- How will you measure its success? _____
  _____
  _____
  _____

PEOPLE

- Who is the character or characters? _____

- Where are they in their lives? _____

- What are they struggling with? _____

- What is their flawed belief about the world or themselves? _____

PROBLEM

- What happens that creates a new problem for them? _____

- Who or what comes along to help them? _____

- How do they finally accomplish their goal? _____

- How do they change as a result? _____

STORY TITLE:

PURPOSE

• Who are you telling this story to? _____
_____
_____
_____

• What is the emotion you want them to feel? _____
_____
_____
_____

• What is the message you want them to receive? _____
_____
_____
_____

• What action do you want your audience to take? _____
_____
_____
_____

PLATFORM

• What format will you use to tell this story? _____
_____
_____
_____

• On which platform will you distribute it? _____
_____
_____
_____

• How can you creatively repurpose it? _____
_____
_____
_____

• How will you measure its success? _____
_____
_____
_____

DATE:

PEOPLE

- Who is the character or characters? _____
  _____
  _____
  _____

- Where are they in their lives? _____
  _____
  _____
  _____

- What are they struggling with? _____
  _____
  _____
  _____

- What is their flawed belief about the world or themselves? _____
  _____
  _____
  _____

PROBLEM

- What happens that creates a new problem for them? _____
  _____
  _____
  _____

- Who or what comes along to help them? _____
  _____
  _____
  _____

- How do they finally accomplish their goal? _____
  _____
  _____
  _____

- How do they change as a result? _____
  _____
  _____
  _____

STORY TITLE:

PURPOSE

- Who are you telling this story to? _____
_____
_____

- What is the emotion you want them to feel? _____
_____
_____

- What is the message you want them to receive? _____
_____
_____

- What action do you want your audience to take? _____
_____
_____

PLATFORM

- What format will you use to tell this story? _____
_____
_____

- On which platform will you distribute it? _____
_____
_____

- How can you creatively repurpose it? _____
_____
_____

- How will you measure its success? _____
_____
_____

DATE:

PEOPLE

- Who is the character or characters?

- Where are they in their lives?

- What are they struggling with?

- What is their flawed belief about the world or themselves?

PROBLEM

- What happens that creates a new problem for them?

- Who or what comes along to help them?

- How do they finally accomplish their goal?

- How do they change as a result?

STORY TITLE:

PURPOSE

- Who are you telling this story to? _____
  _____
  _____
  _____

- What is the emotion you want them to feel? _____
  _____
  _____
  _____

- What is the message you want them to receive? _____
  _____
  _____
  _____

- What action do you want your audience to take? _____
  _____
  _____
  _____

PLATFORM

- What format will you use to tell this story? _____
  _____
  _____
  _____

- On which platform will you distribute it? _____
  _____
  _____
  _____

- How can you creatively repurpose it? _____
  _____
  _____
  _____

- How will you measure its success? _____
  _____
  _____
  _____

PEOPLE

- Who is the character or characters? _____
  _____
  _____
  _____

- Where are they in their lives? _____
  _____
  _____
  _____

- What are they struggling with? _____
  _____
  _____
  _____

- What is their flawed belief about the world or themselves? _____
  _____
  _____
  _____

PROBLEM

- What happens that creates a new problem for them? _____
  _____
  _____
  _____

- Who or what comes along to help them? _____
  _____
  _____
  _____

- How do they finally accomplish their goal? _____
  _____
  _____
  _____

- How do they change as a result? _____
  _____
  _____
  _____

STORY TITLE:

PURPOSE

- Who are you telling this story to? _____

- What is the emotion you want them to feel? _____

- What is the message you want them to receive? _____

- What action do you want your audience to take? _____

PLATFORM

- What format will you use to tell this story? _____

- On which platform will you distribute it? _____

- How can you creatively repurpose it? _____

- How will you measure its success? _____

PEOPLE

- Who is the character or characters? _____
  _____
  _____
  _____

- Where are they in their lives? _____
  _____
  _____
  _____

- What are they struggling with? _____
  _____
  _____
  _____

- What is their flawed belief about the world or themselves? _____
  _____
  _____
  _____

PROBLEM

- What happens that creates a new problem for them? _____
  _____
  _____
  _____

- Who or what comes along to help them? _____
  _____
  _____
  _____

- How do they finally accomplish their goal? _____
  _____
  _____
  _____

- How do they change as a result? _____
  _____
  _____
  _____

STORY TITLE:

PURPOSE

- Who are you telling this story to? _____
  _____
  _____
  _____

- What is the emotion you want them to feel? _____
  _____
  _____
  _____

- What is the message you want them to receive? _____
  _____
  _____

- What action do you want your audience to take? _____
  _____
  _____
  _____

PLATFORM

- What format will you use to tell this story? _____
  _____
  _____
  _____

- On which platform will you distribute it? _____
  _____
  _____
  _____

- How can you creatively repurpose it? _____
  _____
  _____

- How will you measure its success? _____
  _____
  _____
  _____

DATE:

PEOPLE

- Who is the character or characters? _____
  _____
  _____
  _____

- Where are they in their lives? _____
  _____
  _____
  _____

- What are they struggling with? _____
  _____
  _____
  _____

- What is their flawed belief about the world or themselves? _____
  _____
  _____
  _____

PROBLEM

- What happens that creates a new problem for them? _____
  _____
  _____
  _____

- Who or what comes along to help them? _____
  _____
  _____
  _____

- How do they finally accomplish their goal? _____
  _____
  _____
  _____

- How do they change as a result? _____
  _____
  _____
  _____

STORY TITLE:

PURPOSE

- Who are you telling this story to? _____
_____
_____
_____

- What is the emotion you want them to feel? _____
_____
_____
_____

- What is the message you want them to receive? _____
_____
_____
_____

- What action do you want your audience to take? _____
_____
_____
_____

PLATFORM

- What format will you use to tell this story? _____
_____
_____
_____

- On which platform will you distribute it? _____
_____
_____
_____

- How can you creatively repurpose it? _____
_____
_____
_____

- How will you measure its success? _____
_____
_____
_____

PEOPLE

- Who is the character or characters? _____
  _____
  _____
  _____

- Where are they in their lives? _____
  _____
  _____
  _____

- What are they struggling with? _____
  _____
  _____
  _____

- What is their flawed belief about the world or themselves? _____
  _____
  _____
  _____

PROBLEM

- What happens that creates a new problem for them? _____
  _____
  _____
  _____

- Who or what comes along to help them? _____
  _____
  _____
  _____

- How do they finally accomplish their goal? _____
  _____
  _____
  _____

- How do they change as a result? _____
  _____
  _____
  _____

STORY TITLE:

PURPOSE

• Who are you telling this story to? _____
_____
_____

• What is the emotion you want them to feel? _____
_____
_____

• What is the message you want them to receive? _____
_____
_____

• What action do you want your audience to take? _____
_____
_____

PLATFORM

• What format will you use to tell this story? _____
_____
_____

• On which platform will you distribute it? _____
_____
_____

• How can you creatively repurpose it? _____
_____
_____

• How will you measure its success? _____
_____
_____

PEOPLE

- Who is the character or characters? _____
  _____
  _____
  _____

- Where are they in their lives? _____
  _____
  _____
  _____

- What are they struggling with? _____
  _____
  _____
  _____

- What is their flawed belief about the world or themselves? _____
  _____
  _____
  _____

PROBLEM

- What happens that creates a new problem for them? _____
  _____
  _____
  _____

- Who or what comes along to help them? _____
  _____
  _____
  _____

- How do they finally accomplish their goal? _____
  _____
  _____
  _____

- How do they change as a result? _____
  _____
  _____
  _____

STORY TITLE:

PURPOSE

- Who are you telling this story to? _____
_____
_____
_____

- What is the emotion you want them to feel? _____
_____
_____
_____

- What is the message you want them to receive? _____
_____
_____
_____

- What action do you want your audience to take? _____
_____
_____
_____

PLATFORM

- What format will you use to tell this story? _____
_____
_____
_____

- On which platform will you distribute it? _____
_____
_____
_____

- How can you creatively repurpose it? _____
_____
_____
_____

- How will you measure its success? _____
_____
_____
_____

PEOPLE

- Who is the character or characters? _____
  _____
  _____
  _____

- Where are they in their lives? _____
  _____
  _____
  _____

- What are they struggling with? _____
  _____
  _____
  _____

- What is their flawed belief about the world or themselves? _____
  _____
  _____
  _____

PROBLEM

- What happens that creates a new problem for them? _____
  _____
  _____
  _____

- Who or what comes along to help them? _____
  _____
  _____
  _____

- How do they finally accomplish their goal? _____
  _____
  _____
  _____

- How do they change as a result? _____
  _____
  _____
  _____

STORY TITLE:

PURPOSE

- Who are you telling this story to? _____
_____
_____

- What is the emotion you want them to feel? _____
_____
_____

- What is the message you want them to receive? _____
_____
_____

- What action do you want your audience to take? _____
_____
_____

PLATFORM

- What format will you use to tell this story? _____
_____
_____

- On which platform will you distribute it? _____
_____
_____

- How can you creatively repurpose it? _____
_____
_____

- How will you measure its success? _____
_____
_____

PEOPLE

- Who is the character or characters? _____
  _____
  _____

- Where are they in their lives? _____
  _____
  _____

- What are they struggling with? _____
  _____
  _____

- What is their flawed belief about the world or themselves? _____
  _____
  _____
  _____

PROBLEM

- What happens that creates a new problem for them? _____
  _____
  _____

- Who or what comes along to help them? _____
  _____
  _____

- How do they finally accomplish their goal? _____
  _____
  _____

- How do they change as a result? _____
  _____
  _____

STORY TITLE:

PURPOSE

- Who are you telling this story to? _____
  _____
  _____
  _____

- What is the emotion you want them to feel? _____
  _____
  _____
  _____

- What is the message you want them to receive? _____
  _____
  _____
  _____

- What action do you want your audience to take? _____
  _____
  _____
  _____

PLATFORM

- What format will you use to tell this story? _____
  _____
  _____
  _____

- On which platform will you distribute it? _____
  _____
  _____
  _____

- How can you creatively repurpose it? _____
  _____
  _____
  _____

- How will you measure its success? _____
  _____
  _____
  _____

PEOPLE

- Who is the character or characters? _____
  _____
  _____
  _____

- Where are they in their lives? _____
  _____
  _____
  _____

- What are they struggling with? _____
  _____
  _____
  _____

- What is their flawed belief about the world or themselves? _____
  _____
  _____
  _____

PROBLEM

- What happens that creates a new problem for them? _____
  _____
  _____
  _____

- Who or what comes along to help them? _____
  _____
  _____
  _____

- How do they finally accomplish their goal? _____
  _____
  _____
  _____

- How do they change as a result? _____
  _____
  _____
  _____

STORY TITLE:

PURPOSE

- Who are you telling this story to? _____
  _____
  _____
  _____

- What is the emotion you want them to feel? _____
  _____
  _____
  _____

- What is the message you want them to receive? _____
  _____
  _____
  _____

- What action do you want your audience to take? _____
  _____
  _____
  _____

PLATFORM

- What format will you use to tell this story? _____
  _____
  _____
  _____

- On which platform will you distribute it? _____
  _____
  _____
  _____

- How can you creatively repurpose it? _____
  _____
  _____
  _____

- How will you measure its success? _____
  _____
  _____

PEOPLE

- Who is the character or characters? _____
  _____
  _____
  _____

- Where are they in their lives? _____
  _____
  _____
  _____

- What are they struggling with? _____
  _____
  _____
  _____

- What is their flawed belief about the world or themselves? _____
  _____
  _____
  _____

PROBLEM

- What happens that creates a new problem for them? _____
  _____
  _____
  _____

- Who or what comes along to help them? _____
  _____
  _____
  _____

- How do they finally accomplish their goal? _____
  _____
  _____
  _____

- How do they change as a result? _____
  _____
  _____
  _____

STORY TITLE:

PURPOSE

- Who are you telling this story to? _____

- What is the emotion you want them to feel? _____

- What is the message you want them to receive? _____

- What action do you want your audience to take? _____

PLATFORM

- What format will you use to tell this story? _____

- On which platform will you distribute it? _____

- How can you creatively repurpose it? _____

- How will you measure its success? _____

PEOPLE

- Who is the character or characters? _____
  _____
  _____

- Where are they in their lives? _____
  _____
  _____

- What are they struggling with? _____
  _____
  _____

- What is their flawed belief about the world or themselves? _____
  _____
  _____

PROBLEM

- What happens that creates a new problem for them? _____
  _____
  _____

- Who or what comes along to help them? _____
  _____
  _____

- How do they finally accomplish their goal? _____
  _____
  _____

- How do they change as a result? _____
  _____
  _____

STORY TITLE:

PURPOSE

- Who are you telling this story to? _____

- What is the emotion you want them to feel? _____

- What is the message you want them to receive? _____

- What action do you want your audience to take? _____

PLATFORM

- What format will you use to tell this story? _____

- On which platform will you distribute it? _____

- How can you creatively repurpose it? _____

- How will you measure its success? _____

PEOPLE

- Who is the character or characters? _____
  _____
  _____
  _____

- Where are they in their lives? _____
  _____
  _____
  _____

- What are they struggling with? _____
  _____
  _____
  _____

- What is their flawed belief about the world or themselves? _____
  _____
  _____
  _____

PROBLEM

- What happens that creates a new problem for them? _____
  _____
  _____
  _____

- Who or what comes along to help them? _____
  _____
  _____
  _____

- How do they finally accomplish their goal? _____
  _____
  _____
  _____

- How do they change as a result? _____
  _____
  _____
  _____

STORY TITLE:

PURPOSE

- Who are you telling this story to? _____
_____
_____
_____

- What is the emotion you want them to feel? _____
_____
_____
_____

- What is the message you want them to receive? _____
_____
_____
_____

- What action do you want your audience to take? _____
_____
_____
_____

PLATFORM

- What format will you use to tell this story? _____
_____
_____
_____

- On which platform will you distribute it? _____
_____
_____
_____

- How can you creatively repurpose it? _____
_____
_____
_____

- How will you measure its success? _____
_____
_____

DATE:

PEOPLE

- Who is the character or characters? _____

- Where are they in their lives? _____

- What are they struggling with? _____

- What is their flawed belief about the world or themselves? _____

PROBLEM

- What happens that creates a new problem for them? _____

- Who or what comes along to help them? _____

- How do they finally accomplish their goal? _____

- How do they change as a result? _____

STORY TITLE:

PURPOSE

- Who are you telling this story to? _____
_____
_____

- What is the emotion you want them to feel? _____
_____
_____

- What is the message you want them to receive? _____
_____
_____

- What action do you want your audience to take? _____
_____
_____

PLATFORM

- What format will you use to tell this story? _____
_____
_____

- On which platform will you distribute it? _____
_____
_____

- How can you creatively repurpose it? _____
_____
_____

- How will you measure its success? _____
_____
_____

PEOPLE

- Who is the character or characters? _____
  _____
  _____

- Where are they in their lives? _____
  _____
  _____

- What are they struggling with? _____
  _____
  _____

- What is their flawed belief about the world or themselves? _____
  _____
  _____

PROBLEM

- What happens that creates a new problem for them? _____
  _____
  _____

- Who or what comes along to help them? _____
  _____
  _____

- How do they finally accomplish their goal? _____
  _____
  _____

- How do they change as a result? _____
  _____
  _____

STORY TITLE:

PURPOSE

- Who are you telling this story to? _____
  _____
  _____

- What is the emotion you want them to feel? _____
  _____
  _____

- What is the message you want them to receive? _____
  _____
  _____

- What action do you want your audience to take? _____
  _____
  _____

PLATFORM

- What format will you use to tell this story? _____
  _____
  _____

- On which platform will you distribute it? _____
  _____
  _____

- How can you creatively repurpose it? _____
  _____
  _____

How will you measure its success? _____
  _____
  _____

PEOPLE

- Who is the character or characters? _____
  _____
  _____
  _____

- Where are they in their lives? _____
  _____
  _____
  _____

- What are they struggling with? _____
  _____
  _____
  _____

- What is their flawed belief about the world or themselves? _____
  _____
  _____
  _____

PROBLEM

- What happens that creates a new problem for them? _____
  _____
  _____
  _____

- Who or what comes along to help them? _____
  _____
  _____
  _____

- How do they finally accomplish their goal? _____
  _____
  _____
  _____

- How do they change as a result? _____
  _____
  _____
  _____

STORY TITLE:

PURPOSE

- Who are you telling this story to? _____
_____
_____
_____

- What is the emotion you want them to feel? _____
_____
_____
_____

- What is the message you want them to receive? _____
_____
_____
_____

- What action do you want your audience to take? _____
_____
_____
_____

PLATFORM

- What format will you use to tell this story? _____
_____
_____
_____

- On which platform will you distribute it? _____
_____
_____
_____

- How can you creatively repurpose it? _____
_____
_____
_____

- How will you measure its success? _____
_____
_____
_____

DATE:

PEOPLE

- Who is the character or characters? _____
  _____
  _____
  _____

- Where are they in their lives? _____
  _____
  _____
  _____

- What are they struggling with? _____
  _____
  _____
  _____

- What is their flawed belief about the world or themselves? _____
  _____
  _____
  _____

PROBLEM

- What happens that creates a new problem for them? _____
  _____
  _____
  _____

- Who or what comes along to help them? _____
  _____
  _____
  _____

- How do they finally accomplish their goal? _____
  _____
  _____
  _____

- How do they change as a result? _____
  _____
  _____
  _____

STORY TITLE:

PURPOSE

- Who are you telling this story to? _____
_____
_____
_____

- What is the emotion you want them to feel? _____
_____
_____
_____

- What is the message you want them to receive? _____
_____
_____
_____

- What action do you want your audience to take? _____
_____
_____
_____

PLATFORM

- What format will you use to tell this story? _____
_____
_____
_____

- On which platform will you distribute it? _____
_____
_____
_____

- How can you creatively repurpose it? _____
_____
_____
_____

- How will you measure its success? _____
_____
_____
_____

PEOPLE

- Who is the character or characters? _____
  _____
  _____
  _____

- Where are they in their lives? _____
  _____
  _____
  _____

- What are they struggling with? _____
  _____
  _____
  _____

- What is their flawed belief about the world or themselves? _____
  _____
  _____
  _____

PROBLEM

- What happens that creates a new problem for them? _____
  _____
  _____
  _____

- Who or what comes along to help them? _____
  _____
  _____
  _____

- How do they finally accomplish their goal? _____
  _____
  _____
  _____

- How do they change as a result? _____
  _____
  _____
  _____

STORY TITLE:

PURPOSE

- Who are you telling this story to? _____
_____
_____

- What is the emotion you want them to feel? _____
_____
_____

- What is the message you want them to receive? _____
_____
_____

- What action do you want your audience to take? _____
_____
_____

PLATFORM

- What format will you use to tell this story? _____
_____
_____

- On which platform will you distribute it? _____
_____
_____

- How can you creatively repurpose it? _____
_____
_____

- How will you measure its success? _____
_____
_____

DATE:

PEOPLE

- Who is the character or characters? _____
_____
_____
_____

- Where are they in their lives? _____
_____
_____
_____

- What are they struggling with? _____
_____
_____
_____

- What is their flawed belief about the world or themselves? _____
_____
_____
_____

PROBLEM

- What happens that creates a new problem for them? _____
_____
_____
_____

- Who or what comes along to help them? _____
_____
_____
_____

- How do they finally accomplish their goal? _____
_____
_____
_____

- How do they change as a result? _____
_____
_____
_____

STORY TITLE:

PURPOSE

- Who are you telling this story to? _____
  _____
  _____
  _____

- What is the emotion you want them to feel? _____
  _____
  _____
  _____

- What is the message you want them to receive? _____
  _____
  _____
  _____

- What action do you want your audience to take? _____
  _____
  _____
  _____

PLATFORM

- What format will you use to tell this story? _____
  _____
  _____
  _____

- On which platform will you distribute it? _____
  _____
  _____
  _____

- How can you creatively repurpose it? _____
  _____
  _____
  _____

- How will you measure its success? _____
  _____
  _____
  _____

PEOPLE

- Who is the character or characters? _____

- Where are they in their lives? _____

- What are they struggling with? _____

- What is their flawed belief about the world or themselves? _____

PROBLEM

- What happens that creates a new problem for them? _____

- Who or what comes along to help them? _____

- How do they finally accomplish their goal? _____

- How do they change as a result? _____

STORY TITLE:

PURPOSE

- Who are you telling this story to? _____
  _____
  _____
  _____

- What is the emotion you want them to feel? _____
  _____
  _____
  _____

- What is the message you want them to receive? _____
  _____
  _____
  _____

- What action do you want your audience to take? _____
  _____
  _____
  _____

PLATFORM

- What format will you use to tell this story? _____
  _____
  _____
  _____

- On which platform will you distribute it? _____
  _____
  _____
  _____

- How can you creatively repurpose it? _____
  _____
  _____
  _____

- How will you measure its success? _____
  _____
  _____
  _____

DATE:

PEOPLE

- Who is the character or characters? _____
_____
_____
_____

- Where are they in their lives? _____
_____
_____
_____

- What are they struggling with? _____
_____
_____
_____

- What is their flawed belief about the world or themselves? _____
_____
_____
_____

PROBLEM

- What happens that creates a new problem for them? _____
_____
_____
_____

- Who or what comes along to help them? _____
_____
_____
_____

- How do they finally accomplish their goal? _____
_____
_____
_____

- How do they change as a result? _____
_____
_____
_____

STORY TITLE:

PURPOSE

- Who are you telling this story to? _____
_____
_____

- What is the emotion you want them to feel? _____
_____
_____

- What is the message you want them to receive? _____
_____
_____

- What action do you want your audience to take? _____
_____
_____

PLATFORM

- What format will you use to tell this story? _____
_____
_____

- On which platform will you distribute it? _____
_____
_____

- How can you creatively repurpose it? _____
_____
_____

- How will you measure its success? _____
_____
_____

DATE:

PEOPLE

- Who is the character or characters? _____
_____
_____
_____

- Where are they in their lives? _____
_____
_____
_____

- What are they struggling with? _____
_____
_____
_____

- What is their flawed belief about the world or themselves? _____
_____
_____
_____

PROBLEM

- What happens that creates a new problem for them? _____
_____
_____
_____

- Who or what comes along to help them? _____
_____
_____
_____

- How do they finally accomplish their goal? _____
_____
_____
_____

- How do they change as a result? _____
_____
_____
_____

STORY TITLE:

PURPOSE

- Who are you telling this story to? _____
  _____
  _____
  _____

- What is the emotion you want them to feel? _____
  _____
  _____
  _____

- What is the message you want them to receive? _____
  _____
  _____
  _____

- What action do you want your audience to take? _____
  _____
  _____
  _____

PLATFORM

- What format will you use to tell this story? _____
  _____
  _____
  _____

- On which platform will you distribute it? _____
  _____
  _____
  _____

- How can you creatively repurpose it? _____
  _____
  _____
  _____

- How will you measure its success? _____
  _____
  _____
  _____

PEOPLE

- Who is the character or characters? _____
  _____
  _____

- Where are they in their lives? _____
  _____
  _____

- What are they struggling with? _____
  _____
  _____

- What is their flawed belief about the world or themselves? _____
  _____
  _____

PROBLEM

- What happens that creates a new problem for them? _____
  _____
  _____

- Who or what comes along to help them? _____
  _____
  _____

- How do they finally accomplish their goal? _____
  _____
  _____

- How do they change as a result? _____
  _____
  _____

(STORY TITLE:)

- Who are you telling this story to? _____
_____
_____
_____

- What is the emotion you want them to feel? _____
_____
_____
_____

- What is the message you want them to receive? _____
_____
_____
_____

- What action do you want your audience to take? _____
_____
_____
_____

(PLATFORM)

- What format will you use to tell this story? _____
_____
_____
_____

- On which platform will you distribute it? _____
_____
_____
_____

- How can you creatively repurpose it? _____
_____
_____
_____

- How will you measure its success? _____
_____
_____
_____

PEOPLE

- Who is the character or characters? _____

- Where are they in their lives? _____

- What are they struggling with? _____

- What is their flawed belief about the world or themselves? _____

PROBLEM

- What happens that creates a new problem for them? _____

- Who or what comes along to help them? _____

- How do they finally accomplish their goal? _____

- How do they change as a result? _____

STORY TITLE:

PURPOSE

- Who are you telling this story to? _____
_____
_____

- What is the emotion you want them to feel? _____
_____
_____

- What is the message you want them to receive? _____
_____
_____

- What action do you want your audience to take? _____
_____
_____

PLATFORM

- What format will you use to tell this story? _____
_____
_____

- On which platform will you distribute it? _____
_____
_____

- How can you creatively repurpose it? _____
_____
_____

- How will you measure its success? _____
_____
_____

DATE:

PEOPLE

- Who is the character or characters? _____
  _____
  _____
  _____

- Where are they in their lives? _____
  _____
  _____
  _____

- What are they struggling with? _____
  _____
  _____
  _____

- What is their flawed belief about the world or themselves? _____
  _____
  _____
  _____

PROBLEM

- What happens that creates a new problem for them? _____
  _____
  _____
  _____

- Who or what comes along to help them? _____
  _____
  _____
  _____

- How do they finally accomplish their goal? _____
  _____
  _____
  _____

- How do they change as a result? _____
  _____
  _____
  _____

STORY TITLE:

PURPOSE

- Who are you telling this story to? _____
_____
_____
_____

- What is the emotion you want them to feel? _____
_____
_____
_____

- What is the message you want them to receive? _____
_____
_____
_____

- What action do you want your audience to take? _____
_____
_____
_____

PLATFORM

- What format will you use to tell this story? _____
_____
_____
_____

- On which platform will you distribute it? _____
_____
_____
_____

- How can you creatively repurpose it? _____
_____
_____
_____

- How will you measure its success? _____
_____
_____
_____

PEOPLE

- Who is the character or characters? _____
  _____
  _____
  _____

- Where are they in their lives? _____
  _____
  _____
  _____

- What are they struggling with? _____
  _____
  _____
  _____

- What is their flawed belief about the world or themselves? _____
  _____
  _____
  _____

PROBLEM

- What happens that creates a new problem for them? _____
  _____
  _____
  _____

- Who or what comes along to help them? _____
  _____
  _____
  _____

- How do they finally accomplish their goal? _____
  _____
  _____
  _____

- How do they change as a result? _____
  _____
  _____
  _____

STORY TITLE:

PURPOSE

• Who are you telling this story to? _____
_____
_____
_____

• What is the emotion you want them to feel? _____
_____
_____
_____

• What is the message you want them to receive? _____
_____
_____
_____

• What action do you want your audience to take? _____
_____
_____
_____

PLATFORM

• What format will you use to tell this story? _____
_____
_____
_____

• On which platform will you distribute it? _____
_____
_____
_____

• How can you creatively repurpose it? _____
_____
_____
_____

• How will you measure its success? _____
_____
_____
_____

DATE:

PEOPLE

- Who is the character or characters? _____
  _____
  _____
  _____

- Where are they in their lives? _____
  _____
  _____
  _____

- What are they struggling with? _____
  _____
  _____
  _____

- What is their flawed belief about the world or themselves? _____
  _____
  _____
  _____

PROBLEM

- What happens that creates a new problem for them? _____
  _____
  _____
  _____

- Who or what comes along to help them? _____
  _____
  _____
  _____

- How do they finally accomplish their goal? _____
  _____
  _____
  _____

- How do they change as a result? _____
  _____
  _____
  _____

STORY TITLE:

PURPOSE

• Who are you telling this story to? _____

_____

_____

_____

• What is the emotion you want them to feel? _____

_____

_____

_____

• What is the message you want them to receive? _____

_____

_____

_____

• What action do you want your audience to take? _____

_____

_____

_____

PLATFORM

• What format will you use to tell this story? _____

_____

_____

_____

• On which platform will you distribute it? _____

_____

_____

_____

• How can you creatively repurpose it? _____

_____

_____

_____

• How will you measure its success? _____

_____

_____

_____

DATE:

PEOPLE

- Who is the character or characters? _____
  _____
  _____
  _____

- Where are they in their lives? _____
  _____
  _____
  _____

- What are they struggling with? _____
  _____
  _____
  _____

- What is their flawed belief about the world or themselves? _____
  _____
  _____
  _____

PROBLEM

- What happens that creates a new problem for them? _____
  _____
  _____
  _____

- Who or what comes along to help them? _____
  _____
  _____
  _____

- How do they finally accomplish their goal? _____
  _____
  _____
  _____

- How do they change as a result? _____
  _____
  _____
  _____

STORY TITLE:

PURPOSE

- Who are you telling this story to? _____
  _____
  _____
  _____

- What is the emotion you want them to feel? _____
  _____
  _____
  _____

- What is the message you want them to receive? _____
  _____
  _____
  _____

- What action do you want your audience to take? _____
  _____
  _____
  _____

PLATFORM

- What format will you use to tell this story? _____
  _____
  _____
  _____

- On which platform will you distribute it? _____
  _____
  _____
  _____

- How can you creatively repurpose it? _____
  _____
  _____
  _____

- How will you measure its success? _____
  _____
  _____
  _____

DATE:

PEOPLE

- Who is the character or characters? _____
_____
_____
_____

- Where are they in their lives? _____
_____
_____
_____

- What are they struggling with? _____
_____
_____
_____

- What is their flawed belief about the world or themselves? _____
_____
_____
_____

PROBLEM

- What happens that creates a new problem for them? _____
_____
_____
_____

- Who or what comes along to help them? _____
_____
_____
_____

- How do they finally accomplish their goal? _____
_____
_____
_____

- How do they change as a result? _____
_____
_____
_____

STORY TITLE:

PURPOSE

- Who are you telling this story to? _____
_____
_____
_____

- What is the emotion you want them to feel? _____
_____
_____
_____

- What is the message you want them to receive? _____
_____
_____
_____

- What action do you want your audience to take? _____
_____
_____
_____

PLATFORM

- What format will you use to tell this story? _____
_____
_____
_____

- On which platform will you distribute it? _____
_____
_____
_____

- How can you creatively repurpose it? _____
_____
_____
_____

- How will you measure its success? _____
_____
_____
_____

PEOPLE

- Who is the character or characters? _____
  _____
  _____

- Where are they in their lives? _____
  _____
  _____

- What are they struggling with? _____
  _____
  _____

- What is their flawed belief about the world or themselves? _____
  _____
  _____

PROBLEM

- What happens that creates a new problem for them? _____
  _____
  _____
  _____

- Who or what comes along to help them? _____
  _____
  _____
  _____

- How do they finally accomplish their goal? _____
  _____
  _____
  _____

- How do they change as a result? _____
  _____
  _____

STORY TITLE:

PURPOSE

- Who are you telling this story to? _____

_____

_____

- What is the emotion you want them to feel? _____

_____

_____

- What is the message you want them to receive? _____

_____

_____

- What action do you want your audience to take? _____

_____

_____

PLATFORM

- What format will you use to tell this story? _____

_____

_____

- On which platform will you distribute it? _____

_____

_____

- How can you creatively repurpose it? _____

_____

_____

- How will you measure its success? _____

_____

_____

DATE:

PEOPLE

- Who is the character or characters? _____
  _____
  _____
  _____

- Where are they in their lives? _____
  _____
  _____
  _____

- What are they struggling with? _____
  _____
  _____
  _____

- What is their flawed belief about the world or themselves? _____
  _____
  _____
  _____

PROBLEM

- What happens that creates a new problem for them? _____
  _____
  _____
  _____

- Who or what comes along to help them? _____
  _____
  _____
  _____

- How do they finally accomplish their goal? _____
  _____
  _____
  _____

- How do they change as a result? _____
  _____
  _____
  _____

STORY TITLE:

PURPOSE

• Who are you telling this story to? _____
_____
_____
_____

• What is the emotion you want them to feel? _____
_____
_____
_____

• What is the message you want them to receive? _____
_____
_____
_____

• What action do you want your audience to take? _____
_____
_____
_____

PLATFORM

• What format will you use to tell this story? _____
_____
_____
_____

• On which platform will you distribute it? _____
_____
_____
_____

• How can you creatively repurpose it? _____
_____
_____
_____

• How will you measure its success? _____
_____
_____

DATE:

PEOPLE

- Who is the character or characters? _____
  _____
  _____

- Where are they in their lives? _____
  _____
  _____

- What are they struggling with? _____
  _____
  _____

- What is their flawed belief about the world or themselves? _____
  _____
  _____

PROBLEM

- What happens that creates a new problem for them? _____
  _____
  _____

- Who or what comes along to help them? _____
  _____
  _____

- How do they finally accomplish their goal? _____
  _____
  _____

- How do they change as a result? _____
  _____
  _____

STORY TITLE:

PURPOSE

- Who are you telling this story to? _____
_____
_____
_____

- What is the emotion you want them to feel? _____
_____
_____
_____

- What is the message you want them to receive? _____
_____
_____
_____

- What action do you want your audience to take? _____
_____
_____
_____

PLATFORM

- What format will you use to tell this story? _____
_____
_____
_____

- On which platform will you distribute it? _____
_____
_____
_____

- How can you creatively repurpose it? _____
_____
_____
_____

- How will you measure its success? _____
_____
_____
_____

PEOPLE

- Who is the character or characters? _____
  _____
  _____
  _____

- Where are they in their lives? _____
  _____
  _____
  _____

- What are they struggling with? _____
  _____
  _____
  _____

- What is their flawed belief about the world or themselves? _____
  _____
  _____
  _____

PROBLEM

- What happens that creates a new problem for them? _____
  _____
  _____
  _____

- Who or what comes along to help them? _____
  _____
  _____
  _____

- How do they finally accomplish their goal? _____
  _____
  _____
  _____

- How do they change as a result? _____
  _____
  _____
  _____

STORY TITLE:

PURPOSE

- Who are you telling this story to? _____

_____

_____

_____

- What is the emotion you want them to feel? _____

_____

_____

_____

- What is the message you want them to receive? _____

_____

_____

_____

- What action do you want your audience to take? _____

_____

_____

_____

PLATFORM

- What format will you use to tell this story? _____

_____

_____

_____

- On which platform will you distribute it? _____

_____

_____

_____

- How can you creatively repurpose it? _____

_____

_____

_____

- How will you measure its success? _____

_____

_____

_____

PEOPLE

- Who is the character or characters? _____
  _____
  _____
  _____

- Where are they in their lives? _____
  _____
  _____
  _____

- What are they struggling with? _____
  _____
  _____
  _____

- What is their flawed belief about the world or themselves? _____
  _____
  _____
  _____

PROBLEM

- What happens that creates a new problem for them? _____
  _____
  _____
  _____

- Who or what comes along to help them? _____
  _____
  _____
  _____

- How do they finally accomplish their goal? _____
  _____
  _____
  _____

- How do they change as a result? _____
  _____
  _____
  _____

STORY TITLE:

PURPOSE

- Who are you telling this story to? _____

- What is the emotion you want them to feel? _____

- What is the message you want them to receive? _____

- What action do you want your audience to take? _____

PLATFORM

- What format will you use to tell this story? _____

- On which platform will you distribute it? _____

- How can you creatively repurpose it? _____

- How will you measure its success? _____

DATE:

PEOPLE

- Who is the character or characters? _____
_____
_____
_____

- Where are they in their lives? _____
_____
_____
_____

- What are they struggling with? _____
_____
_____
_____

- What is their flawed belief about the world or themselves? _____
_____
_____
_____

PROBLEM

- What happens that creates a new problem for them? _____
_____
_____
_____

- Who or what comes along to help them? _____
_____
_____
_____

- How do they finally accomplish their goal? _____
_____
_____
_____

- How do they change as a result? _____
_____
_____
_____

STORY TITLE:

PURPOSE

- Who are you telling this story to? _____
  _____
  _____
  _____

- What is the emotion you want them to feel? _____
  _____
  _____
  _____

- What is the message you want them to receive? _____
  _____
  _____
  _____

- What action do you want your audience to take? _____
  _____
  _____
  _____

PLATFORM

- What format will you use to tell this story? _____
  _____
  _____
  _____

- On which platform will you distribute it? _____
  _____
  _____
  _____

- How can you creatively repurpose it? _____
  _____
  _____
  _____

- How will you measure its success? _____
  _____
  _____
  _____

PEOPLE

- Who is the character or characters? _____
  _____
  _____
  _____

- Where are they in their lives? _____
  _____
  _____
  _____

- What are they struggling with? _____
  _____
  _____
  _____

- What is their flawed belief about the world or themselves? _____
  _____
  _____
  _____

PROBLEM

- What happens that creates a new problem for them? _____
  _____
  _____
  _____

- Who or what comes along to help them? _____
  _____
  _____
  _____

- How do they finally accomplish their goal? _____
  _____
  _____
  _____

- How do they change as a result? _____
  _____
  _____

STORY TITLE:

PURPOSE

- Who are you telling this story to? _____
  _____
  _____
  _____

- What is the emotion you want them to feel? _____
  _____
  _____
  _____

- What is the message you want them to receive? _____
  _____
  _____
  _____

- What action do you want your audience to take? _____
  _____
  _____
  _____

PLATFORM

- What format will you use to tell this story? _____
  _____
  _____
  _____

- On which platform will you distribute it? _____
  _____
  _____
  _____

- How can you creatively repurpose it? _____
  _____
  _____
  _____

- How will you measure its success? _____
  _____
  _____
  _____

DATE:

PEOPLE

- Who is the character or characters? _____
  _____
  _____
  _____

- Where are they in their lives? _____
  _____
  _____
  _____

- What are they struggling with? _____
  _____
  _____
  _____

- What is their flawed belief about the world or themselves? _____
  _____
  _____
  _____

PROBLEM

- What happens that creates a new problem for them? _____
  _____
  _____
  _____

- Who or what comes along to help them? _____
  _____
  _____
  _____

- How do they finally accomplish their goal? _____
  _____
  _____
  _____

- How do they change as a result? _____
  _____
  _____
  _____

STORY TITLE:

PURPOSE

- Who are you telling this story to? _____
  _____
  _____
  _____

- What is the emotion you want them to feel? _____
  _____
  _____
  _____

- What is the message you want them to receive? _____
  _____
  _____
  _____

- What action do you want your audience to take? _____
  _____
  _____
  _____

PLATFORM

- What format will you use to tell this story? _____
  _____
  _____
  _____

- On which platform will you distribute it? _____
  _____
  _____
  _____

- How can you creatively repurpose it? _____
  _____
  _____
  _____

- How will you measure its success? _____
  _____
  _____
  _____

DATE:

PEOPLE

- Who is the character or characters? _____
_____
_____
_____

- Where are they in their lives? _____
_____
_____
_____

- What are they struggling with? _____
_____
_____
_____

- What is their flawed belief about the world or themselves? _____
_____
_____
_____

PROBLEM

- What happens that creates a new problem for them? _____
_____
_____
_____

- Who or what comes along to help them? _____
_____
_____
_____

- How do they finally accomplish their goal? _____
_____
_____
_____

- How do they change as a result? _____
_____
_____
_____

STORY TITLE:

PURPOSE

- Who are you telling this story to? _____
  _____
  _____
  _____

- What is the emotion you want them to feel? _____
  _____
  _____
  _____

- What is the message you want them to receive? _____
  _____
  _____
  _____

- What action do you want your audience to take? _____
  _____
  _____
  _____

PLATFORM

- What format will you use to tell this story? _____
  _____
  _____
  _____

- On which platform will you distribute it? _____
  _____
  _____
  _____

- How can you creatively repurpose it? _____
  _____
  _____
  _____

- How will you measure its success? _____
  _____
  _____
  _____

DATE:

PEOPLE

- Who is the character or characters? _____
  _____
  _____
  _____

- Where are they in their lives? _____
  _____
  _____
  _____

- What are they struggling with? _____
  _____
  _____
  _____

- What is their flawed belief about the world or themselves? _____
  _____
  _____
  _____

PROBLEM

- What happens that creates a new problem for them? _____
  _____
  _____
  _____

- Who or what comes along to help them? _____
  _____
  _____
  _____

- How do they finally accomplish their goal? _____
  _____
  _____
  _____

- How do they change as a result? _____
  _____
  _____

STORY TITLE:

PURPOSE

- Who are you telling this story to? _____
_____
_____

- What is the emotion you want them to feel? _____
_____
_____

- What is the message you want them to receive? _____
_____
_____

- What action do you want your audience to take? _____
_____
_____

PLATFORM

- What format will you use to tell this story? _____
_____
_____

- On which platform will you distribute it? _____
_____
_____

- How can you creatively repurpose it? _____
_____
_____

- How will you measure its success? _____
_____
_____

PEOPLE

- Who is the character or characters? _____
_____
_____
_____

- Where are they in their lives? _____
_____
_____
_____

- What are they struggling with? _____
_____
_____
_____

- What is their flawed belief about the world or themselves? _____
_____
_____
_____

PROBLEM

- What happens that creates a new problem for them? _____
_____
_____
_____

- Who or what comes along to help them? _____
_____
_____
_____

- How do they finally accomplish their goal? _____
_____
_____
_____

- How do they change as a result? _____
_____
_____

STORY TITLE:

PURPOSE

- Who are you telling this story to? _____
  _____
  _____
  _____

- What is the emotion you want them to feel? _____
  _____
  _____
  _____

- What is the message you want them to receive? _____
  _____
  _____
  _____

- What action do you want your audience to take? _____
  _____
  _____
  _____

PLATFORM

- What format will you use to tell this story? _____
  _____
  _____
  _____

- On which platform will you distribute it? _____
  _____
  _____
  _____

- How can you creatively repurpose it? _____
  _____
  _____
  _____

- How will you measure its success? _____
  _____
  _____
  _____

PEOPLE

- Who is the character or characters? _____

_____

_____

- Where are they in their lives? _____

_____

_____

- What are they struggling with? _____

_____

_____

- What is their flawed belief about the world or themselves? _____

_____

_____

PROBLEM

- What happens that creates a new problem for them? _____

_____

_____

- Who or what comes along to help them? _____

_____

_____

- How do they finally accomplish their goal? _____

_____

_____

- How do they change as a result? _____

_____

_____

STORY TITLE:

PURPOSE

- Who are you telling this story to? _____
  _____
  _____
  _____

- What is the emotion you want them to feel? _____
  _____
  _____
  _____

- What is the message you want them to receive? _____
  _____
  _____
  _____

- What action do you want your audience to take? _____
  _____
  _____
  _____

PLATFORM

- What format will you use to tell this story? _____
  _____
  _____
  _____

- On which platform will you distribute it? _____
  _____
  _____
  _____

- How can you creatively repurpose it? _____
  _____
  _____
  _____

- How will you measure its success? _____
  _____
  _____

PEOPLE

- Who is the character or characters? _____
  _____
  _____
  _____

- Where are they in their lives? _____
  _____
  _____
  _____

- What are they struggling with? _____
  _____
  _____
  _____

- What is their flawed belief about the world or themselves? _____
  _____
  _____
  _____

PROBLEM

- What happens that creates a new problem for them? _____
  _____
  _____
  _____

- Who or what comes along to help them? _____
  _____
  _____
  _____

- How do they finally accomplish their goal? _____
  _____
  _____
  _____

- How do they change as a result? _____
  _____
  _____

STORY TITLE:

PURPOSE

- Who are you telling this story to? _____

- What is the emotion you want them to feel? _____

- What is the message you want them to receive? _____

- What action do you want your audience to take? _____

PLATFORM

- What format will you use to tell this story? _____

- On which platform will you distribute it? _____

- How can you creatively repurpose it? _____

- How will you measure its success? _____

PEOPLE

- Who is the character or characters? _____
  _____
  _____
  _____

- Where are they in their lives? _____
  _____
  _____
  _____

- What are they struggling with? _____
  _____
  _____
  _____

- What is their flawed belief about the world or themselves? _____
  _____
  _____
  _____

PROBLEM

- What happens that creates a new problem for them? _____
  _____
  _____
  _____

- Who or what comes along to help them? _____
  _____
  _____
  _____

- How do they finally accomplish their goal? _____
  _____
  _____
  _____

- How do they change as a result? _____
  _____
  _____
  _____

STORY TITLE:

PURPOSE

- Who are you telling this story to? _____

_____

_____

_____

- What is the emotion you want them to feel? _____

_____

_____

_____

- What is the message you want them to receive? _____

_____

_____

_____

- What action do you want your audience to take? _____

_____

_____

_____

PLATFORM

- What format will you use to tell this story? _____

_____

_____

_____

- On which platform will you distribute it? _____

_____

_____

_____

- How can you creatively repurpose it? _____

_____

_____

_____

- How will you measure its success? _____

_____

_____

_____

PEOPLE

- Who is the character or characters? _____
  _____
  _____
  _____

- Where are they in their lives? _____
  _____
  _____
  _____

- What are they struggling with? _____
  _____
  _____
  _____

- What is their flawed belief about the world or themselves? _____
  _____
  _____
  _____

PROBLEM

- What happens that creates a new problem for them? _____
  _____
  _____
  _____

- Who or what comes along to help them? _____
  _____
  _____
  _____

- How do they finally accomplish their goal? _____
  _____
  _____
  _____

- How do they change as a result? _____
  _____
  _____
  _____

STORY TITLE:

PURPOSE

- Who are you telling this story to? _____
  _____
  _____

- What is the emotion you want them to feel? _____
  _____
  _____

- What is the message you want them to receive? _____
  _____
  _____

- What action do you want your audience to take? _____
  _____
  _____

PLATFORM

- What format will you use to tell this story? _____
  _____
  _____

- On which platform will you distribute it? _____
  _____
  _____

- How can you creatively repurpose it? _____
  _____
  _____

- How will you measure its success? _____
  _____
  _____

PEOPLE

- Who is the character or characters? _____

- Where are they in their lives? _____

- What are they struggling with? _____

- What is their flawed belief about the world or themselves? _____

PROBLEM

- What happens that creates a new problem for them? _____

- Who or what comes along to help them? _____

- How do they finally accomplish their goal? _____

- How do they change as a result? _____

STORY TITLE:

PURPOSE

- Who are you telling this story to? _____
  _____
  _____
  _____

- What is the emotion you want them to feel? _____
  _____
  _____
  _____

- What is the message you want them to receive? _____
  _____
  _____
  _____

- What action do you want your audience to take? _____
  _____
  _____
  _____

PLATFORM

- What format will you use to tell this story? _____
  _____
  _____
  _____

- On which platform will you distribute it? _____
  _____
  _____
  _____

- How can you creatively repurpose it? _____
  _____
  _____
  _____

- How will you measure its success? _____
  _____
  _____
  _____

PEOPLE

- Who is the character or characters? _____
  _____
  _____
  _____

- Where are they in their lives? _____
  _____
  _____
  _____

- What are they struggling with? _____
  _____
  _____
  _____

- What is their flawed belief about the world or themselves? _____
  _____
  _____
  _____

PROBLEM

- What happens that creates a new problem for them? _____
  _____
  _____
  _____

- Who or what comes along to help them? _____
  _____
  _____
  _____

- How do they finally accomplish their goal? _____
  _____
  _____
  _____

- How do they change as a result? _____
  _____
  _____
  _____

STORY TITLE:

PURPOSE

- Who are you telling this story to? _____
  _____
  _____
  _____

- What is the emotion you want them to feel? _____
  _____
  _____
  _____

- What is the message you want them to receive? _____
  _____
  _____
  _____

- What action do you want your audience to take? _____
  _____
  _____
  _____

PLATFORM

- What format will you use to tell this story? _____
  _____
  _____
  _____

- On which platform will you distribute it? _____
  _____
  _____
  _____

- How can you creatively repurpose it? _____
  _____
  _____
  _____

- How will you measure its success? _____
  _____
  _____
  _____

PEOPLE

- Who is the character or characters? _____
  _____
  _____
  _____

- Where are they in their lives? _____
  _____
  _____
  _____

- What are they struggling with? _____
  _____
  _____
  _____

- What is their flawed belief about the world or themselves? _____
  _____
  _____
  _____

PROBLEM

- What happens that creates a new problem for them? _____
  _____
  _____
  _____

- Who or what comes along to help them? _____
  _____
  _____
  _____

- How do they finally accomplish their goal? _____
  _____
  _____
  _____

- How do they change as a result? _____
  _____
  _____
  _____

STORY TITLE:

PURPOSE

- Who are you telling this story to? _____
_____
_____
_____

- What is the emotion you want them to feel? _____
_____
_____
_____

- What is the message you want them to receive? _____
_____
_____
_____

- What action do you want your audience to take? _____
_____
_____
_____

PLATFORM

- What format will you use to tell this story? _____
_____
_____
_____

- On which platform will you distribute it? _____
_____
_____
_____

- How can you creatively repurpose it? _____
_____
_____
_____

- How will you measure its success? _____
_____
_____

PEOPLE

- Who is the character or characters? _____
  _____
  _____

- Where are they in their lives? _____
  _____
  _____

- What are they struggling with? _____
  _____
  _____

- What is their flawed belief about the world or themselves? _____
  _____
  _____

PROBLEM

- What happens that creates a new problem for them? _____
  _____
  _____

- Who or what comes along to help them? _____
  _____
  _____

- How do they finally accomplish their goal? _____
  _____
  _____

- How do they change as a result? _____
  _____
  _____

STORY TITLE:

PURPOSE

• Who are you telling this story to? _____
_____
_____

• What is the emotion you want them to feel? _____
_____
_____

• What is the message you want them to receive? _____
_____
_____

• What action do you want your audience to take? _____
_____
_____

PLATFORM

• What format will you use to tell this story? _____
_____
_____

• On which platform will you distribute it? _____
_____
_____

• How can you creatively repurpose it? _____
_____
_____

• How will you measure its success? _____
_____
_____

PEOPLE

- Who is the character or characters? _____
  _____
  _____
  _____

- Where are they in their lives? _____
  _____
  _____
  _____

- What are they struggling with? _____
  _____
  _____
  _____

- What is their flawed belief about the world or themselves? _____
  _____
  _____
  _____

PROBLEM

- What happens that creates a new problem for them? _____
  _____
  _____
  _____

- Who or what comes along to help them? _____
  _____
  _____
  _____

- How do they finally accomplish their goal? _____
  _____
  _____
  _____

- How do they change as a result? _____
  _____
  _____
  _____

STORY TITLE:

PURPOSE

- Who are you telling this story to? _____
_____
_____
_____

- What is the emotion you want them to feel? _____
_____
_____
_____

- What is the message you want them to receive? _____
_____
_____
_____

- What action do you want your audience to take? _____
_____
_____
_____

PLATFORM

- What format will you use to tell this story? _____
_____
_____
_____

- On which platform will you distribute it? _____
_____
_____
_____

- How can you creatively repurpose it? _____
_____
_____
_____

- How will you measure its success? _____
_____
_____
_____

DATE:

PEOPLE

- Who is the character or characters? _____
_____
_____
_____

- Where are they in their lives? _____
_____
_____
_____

- What are they struggling with? _____
_____
_____
_____

- What is their flawed belief about the world or themselves? _____
_____
_____
_____

PROBLEM

- What happens that creates a new problem for them? _____
_____
_____
_____

- Who or what comes along to help them? _____
_____
_____
_____

- How do they finally accomplish their goal? _____
_____
_____
_____

- How do they change as a result? _____
_____
_____
_____

STORY TITLE:

PURPOSE

- Who are you telling this story to? _____
  _____
  _____
  _____

- What is the emotion you want them to feel? _____
  _____
  _____
  _____

- What is the message you want them to receive? _____
  _____
  _____
  _____

- What action do you want your audience to take? _____
  _____
  _____
  _____

PLATFORM

- What format will you use to tell this story? _____
  _____
  _____
  _____

- On which platform will you distribute it? _____
  _____
  _____
  _____

- How can you creatively repurpose it? _____
  _____
  _____
  _____

- How will you measure its success? _____
  _____
  _____
  _____

PEOPLE

- Who is the character or characters? _____

_____

- Where are they in their lives? _____

_____

- What are they struggling with? _____

_____

- What is their flawed belief about the world or themselves? _____

_____

PROBLEM

- What happens that creates a new problem for them? _____

_____

- Who or what comes along to help them? _____

_____

- How do they finally accomplish their goal? _____

_____

- How do they change as a result? _____

_____

STORY TITLE:

PURPOSE

- Who are you telling this story to? _____
_____
_____

- What is the emotion you want them to feel? _____
_____
_____

- What is the message you want them to receive? _____
_____
_____

- What action do you want your audience to take? _____
_____
_____

PLATFORM

- What format will you use to tell this story? _____
_____
_____

- On which platform will you distribute it? _____
_____
_____

- How can you creatively repurpose it? _____
_____
_____

- How will you measure its success? _____
_____
_____

PEOPLE

- Who is the character or characters? _____

_____

_____

- Where are they in their lives? _____

_____

_____

- What are they struggling with? _____

_____

_____

- What is their flawed belief about the world or themselves? _____

_____

_____

PROBLEM

- What happens that creates a new problem for them? _____

_____

_____

- Who or what comes along to help them? _____

_____

_____

- How do they finally accomplish their goal? _____

_____

_____

- How do they change as a result? _____

_____

_____

STORY TITLE:

PURPOSE

- Who are you telling this story to? _____
_____
_____

- What is the emotion you want them to feel? _____
_____
_____

- What is the message you want them to receive? _____
_____
_____

- What action do you want your audience to take? _____
_____
_____

PLATFORM

- What format will you use to tell this story? _____
_____
_____

- On which platform will you distribute it? _____
_____
_____

- How can you creatively repurpose it? _____
_____
_____

- How will you measure its success? _____
_____
_____

PEOPLE

- Who is the character or characters? _____

_____

_____

- Where are they in their lives? _____

_____

_____

- What are they struggling with? _____

_____

_____

- What is their flawed belief about the world or themselves? _____

_____

_____

PROBLEM

- What happens that creates a new problem for them? _____

_____

_____

- Who or what comes along to help them? _____

_____

_____

- How do they finally accomplish their goal? _____

_____

_____

- How do they change as a result? _____

_____

_____

STORY TITLE:

PURPOSE

- Who are you telling this story to? _____
  _____
  _____
  _____

- What is the emotion you want them to feel? _____
  _____
  _____
  _____

- What is the message you want them to receive? _____
  _____
  _____
  _____

- What action do you want your audience to take? _____
  _____
  _____
  _____

PLATFORM

- What format will you use to tell this story? _____
  _____
  _____
  _____

- On which platform will you distribute it? _____
  _____
  _____
  _____

- How can you creatively repurpose it? _____
  _____
  _____
  _____

- How will you measure its success? _____
  _____
  _____
  _____

PEOPLE

- Who is the character or characters? _____
  _____
  _____
  _____

- Where are they in their lives? _____
  _____
  _____
  _____

- What are they struggling with? _____
  _____
  _____
  _____

- What is their flawed belief about the world or themselves? _____
  _____
  _____
  _____

PROBLEM

- What happens that creates a new problem for them? _____
  _____
  _____
  _____

- Who or what comes along to help them? _____
  _____
  _____
  _____

- How do they finally accomplish their goal? _____
  _____
  _____
  _____

- How do they change as a result? _____
  _____
  _____
  _____

STORY TITLE:

PURPOSE

• Who are you telling this story to? _____

_____

_____

• What is the emotion you want them to feel? _____

_____

_____

• What is the message you want them to receive? _____

_____

_____

• What action do you want your audience to take? _____

_____

_____

PLATFORM

• What format will you use to tell this story? _____

_____

_____

• On which platform will you distribute it? _____

_____

_____

• How can you creatively repurpose it? _____

_____

_____

• How will you measure its success? _____

_____

_____

DATE:

PEOPLE

- Who is the character or characters? _____
  _____
  _____
  _____

- Where are they in their lives? _____
  _____
  _____
  _____

- What are they struggling with? _____
  _____
  _____
  _____

- What is their flawed belief about the world or themselves? _____
  _____
  _____
  _____

PROBLEM

- What happens that creates a new problem for them? _____
  _____
  _____
  _____

- Who or what comes along to help them? _____
  _____
  _____
  _____

- How do they finally accomplish their goal? _____
  _____
  _____
  _____

- How do they change as a result? _____
  _____
  _____

STORY TITLE:

PURPOSE

• Who are you telling this story to? _____
_____
_____
_____

• What is the emotion you want them to feel? _____
_____
_____
_____

• What is the message you want them to receive? _____
_____
_____
_____

• What action do you want your audience to take? _____
_____
_____
_____

PLATFORM

• What format will you use to tell this story? _____
_____
_____
_____

• On which platform will you distribute it? _____
_____
_____
_____

• How can you creatively repurpose it? _____
_____
_____
_____

• How will you measure its success? _____
_____
_____

DATE:

PEOPLE

- Who is the character or characters? _____
_____
_____
_____

- Where are they in their lives? _____
_____
_____
_____

- What are they struggling with? _____
_____
_____
_____

- What is their flawed belief about the world or themselves? _____
_____
_____
_____

PROBLEM

- What happens that creates a new problem for them? _____
_____
_____
_____

- Who or what comes along to help them? _____
_____
_____
_____

- How do they finally accomplish their goal? _____
_____
_____
_____

- How do they change as a result? _____
_____
_____
_____

STORY TITLE:

PURPOSE

- Who are you telling this story to? _____

- What is the emotion you want them to feel? _____

- What is the message you want them to receive? _____

- What action do you want your audience to take? _____

PLATFORM

- What format will you use to tell this story? _____

- On which platform will you distribute it? _____

- How can you creatively repurpose it? _____

- How will you measure its success? _____

PEOPLE

- Who is the character or characters? _____

- Where are they in their lives? _____

- What are they struggling with? _____

- What is their flawed belief about the world or themselves? _____

PROBLEM

- What happens that creates a new problem for them? _____

- Who or what comes along to help them? _____

- How do they finally accomplish their goal? _____

- How do they change as a result? _____

STORY TITLE:

PURPOSE

- Who are you telling this story to? _____
  _____
  _____

- What is the emotion you want them to feel? _____
  _____
  _____

- What is the message you want them to receive? _____
  _____
  _____

- What action do you want your audience to take? _____
  _____
  _____

PLATFORM

- What format will you use to tell this story? _____
  _____
  _____

- On which platform will you distribute it? _____
  _____
  _____

- How can you creatively repurpose it? _____
  _____
  _____

- How will you measure its success? _____
  _____
  _____

PEOPLE

- Who is the character or characters? _____
_____
_____
_____

- Where are they in their lives? _____
_____
_____
_____

- What are they struggling with? _____
_____
_____
_____

- What is their flawed belief about the world or themselves? _____
_____
_____
_____

PROBLEM

- What happens that creates a new problem for them? _____
_____
_____
_____

- Who or what comes along to help them? _____
_____
_____
_____

- How do they finally accomplish their goal? _____
_____
_____
_____

- How do they change as a result? _____
_____
_____
_____

STORY TITLE:

PURPOSE

- Who are you telling this story to? _____
  _____
  _____
  _____

- What is the emotion you want them to feel? _____
  _____
  _____
  _____

- What is the message you want them to receive? _____
  _____
  _____
  _____

- What action do you want your audience to take? _____
  _____
  _____
  _____

PLATFORM

- What format will you use to tell this story? _____
  _____
  _____
  _____

- On which platform will you distribute it? _____
  _____
  _____
  _____

- How can you creatively repurpose it? _____
  _____
  _____
  _____

- How will you measure its success? _____
  _____
  _____

PEOPLE

- Who is the character or characters? _____
_____
_____

- Where are they in their lives? _____
_____
_____

- What are they struggling with? _____
_____
_____

- What is their flawed belief about the world or themselves? _____
_____
_____

PROBLEM

- What happens that creates a new problem for them? _____
_____
_____

- Who or what comes along to help them? _____
_____
_____

- How do they finally accomplish their goal? _____
_____
_____

- How do they change as a result? _____
_____
_____

STORY TITLE:

PURPOSE

- Who are you telling this story to? _____
_____
_____
_____

- What is the emotion you want them to feel? _____
_____
_____
_____

- What is the message you want them to receive? _____
_____
_____
_____

- What action do you want your audience to take? _____
_____
_____
_____

PLATFORM

- What format will you use to tell this story? _____
_____
_____
_____

- On which platform will you distribute it? _____
_____
_____
_____

- How can you creatively repurpose it? _____
_____
_____
_____

- How will you measure its success? _____
_____
_____
_____

DATE:

PEOPLE

- Who is the character or characters? _____

- Where are they in their lives? _____

- What are they struggling with? _____

- What is their flawed belief about the world or themselves? _____

PROBLEM

- What happens that creates a new problem for them? _____

- Who or what comes along to help them? _____

- How do they finally accomplish their goal? _____

- How do they change as a result? _____

STORY TITLE:

PURPOSE

- Who are you telling this story to? _____
  _____
  _____
  _____

- What is the emotion you want them to feel? _____
  _____
  _____
  _____

- What is the message you want them to receive? _____
  _____
  _____
  _____

- What action do you want your audience to take? _____
  _____
  _____
  _____

PLATFORM

- What format will you use to tell this story? _____
  _____
  _____
  _____

- On which platform will you distribute it? _____
  _____
  _____
  _____

- How can you creatively repurpose it? _____
  _____
  _____
  _____

- How will you measure its success? _____
  _____
  _____
  _____

PEOPLE

- Who is the character or characters? _____
  _____
  _____
  _____

- Where are they in their lives? _____
  _____
  _____
  _____

- What are they struggling with? _____
  _____
  _____
  _____

- What is their flawed belief about the world or themselves? _____
  _____
  _____
  _____

PROBLEM

- What happens that creates a new problem for them? _____
  _____
  _____
  _____

- Who or what comes along to help them? _____
  _____
  _____
  _____

- How do they finally accomplish their goal? _____
  _____
  _____
  _____

- How do they change as a result? _____
  _____
  _____
  _____

STORY TITLE:

PURPOSE

- Who are you telling this story to? _____
_____
_____
_____

- What is the emotion you want them to feel? _____
_____
_____
_____

- What is the message you want them to receive? _____
_____
_____
_____

- What action do you want your audience to take? _____
_____
_____
_____

PLATFORM

- What format will you use to tell this story? _____
_____
_____
_____

- On which platform will you distribute it? _____
_____
_____
_____

- How can you creatively repurpose it? _____
_____
_____
_____

- How will you measure its success? _____
_____
_____

DATE:

PEOPLE

- Who is the character or characters? _____
_____
_____

- Where are they in their lives? _____
_____
_____

- What are they struggling with? _____
_____
_____

- What is their flawed belief about the world or themselves? _____
_____
_____
_____

PROBLEM

- What happens that creates a new problem for them? _____
_____
_____

- Who or what comes along to help them? _____
_____
_____

- How do they finally accomplish their goal? _____
_____
_____

- How do they change as a result? _____
_____
_____

STORY TITLE:

PURPOSE

- Who are you telling this story to? _____
_____
_____

- What is the emotion you want them to feel? _____
_____
_____

- What is the message you want them to receive? _____
_____
_____

- What action do you want your audience to take? _____
_____
_____

PLATFORM

- What format will you use to tell this story? _____
_____
_____

- On which platform will you distribute it? _____
_____
_____

- How can you creatively repurpose it? _____
_____
_____

- How will you measure its success? _____
_____
_____

PEOPLE

- Who is the character or characters? _____

- Where are they in their lives? _____

- What are they struggling with? _____

- What is their flawed belief about the world or themselves? _____

PROBLEM

- What happens that creates a new problem for them? _____

- Who or what comes along to help them? _____

- How do they finally accomplish their goal? _____

- How do they change as a result? _____

STORY TITLE:

PURPOSE

- Who are you telling this story to? _____
_____
_____
_____

- What is the emotion you want them to feel? _____
_____
_____
_____

- What is the message you want them to receive? _____
_____
_____
_____

- What action do you want your audience to take? _____
_____
_____
_____

PLATFORM

- What format will you use to tell this story? _____
_____
_____
_____

- On which platform will you distribute it? _____
_____
_____
_____

- How can you creatively repurpose it? _____
_____
_____
_____

- How will you measure its success? _____
_____
_____
_____

DATE:

PEOPLE

- Who is the character or characters? _____
_____
_____
_____

- Where are they in their lives? _____
_____
_____
_____

- What are they struggling with? _____
_____
_____
_____

- What is their flawed belief about the world or themselves? _____
_____
_____
_____

PROBLEM

- What happens that creates a new problem for them? _____
_____
_____
_____

- Who or what comes along to help them? _____
_____
_____
_____

- How do they finally accomplish their goal? _____
_____
_____
_____

- How do they change as a result? _____
_____
_____
_____

STORY TITLE:

PURPOSE

- Who are you telling this story to? _____
_____
_____
_____

- What is the emotion you want them to feel? _____
_____
_____
_____

- What is the message you want them to receive? _____
_____
_____
_____

- What action do you want your audience to take? _____
_____
_____
_____

PLATFORM

- What format will you use to tell this story? _____
_____
_____
_____

- On which platform will you distribute it? _____
_____
_____
_____

- How can you creatively repurpose it? _____
_____
_____
_____

- How will you measure its success? _____
_____
_____

DATE:

PEOPLE

- Who is the character or characters? _____
  _____
  _____
  _____

- Where are they in their lives? _____
  _____
  _____
  _____

- What are they struggling with? _____
  _____
  _____

- What is their flawed belief about the world or themselves? _____
  _____
  _____
  _____

PROBLEM

- What happens that creates a new problem for them? _____
  _____
  _____
  _____

- Who or what comes along to help them? _____
  _____
  _____
  _____

- How do they finally accomplish their goal? _____
  _____
  _____
  _____

- How do they change as a result? _____
  _____
  _____
  _____

[STORY TITLE:]

PURPOSE

- Who are you telling this story to? _____
_____
_____
_____

- What is the emotion you want them to feel? _____
_____
_____
_____

- What is the message you want them to receive? _____
_____
_____
_____

- What action do you want your audience to take? _____
_____
_____
_____

PLATFORM

- What format will you use to tell this story? _____
_____
_____
_____

- On which platform will you distribute it? _____
_____
_____
_____

- How can you creatively repurpose it? _____
_____
_____
_____

- How will you measure its success? _____
_____
_____

PEOPLE

- Who is the character or characters? _____
  _____
  _____
  _____

- Where are they in their lives? _____
  _____
  _____
  _____

- What are they struggling with? _____
  _____
  _____
  _____

- What is their flawed belief about the world or themselves? _____
  _____
  _____
  _____

PROBLEM

- What happens that creates a new problem for them? _____
  _____
  _____
  _____

- Who or what comes along to help them? _____
  _____
  _____
  _____

- How do they finally accomplish their goal? _____
  _____
  _____
  _____

- How do they change as a result? _____
  _____
  _____

STORY TITLE:

PURPOSE

- Who are you telling this story to? _____

- What is the emotion you want them to feel? _____

- What is the message you want them to receive? _____

- What action do you want your audience to take? _____

PLATFORM

- What format will you use to tell this story? _____

- On which platform will you distribute it? _____

- How can you creatively repurpose it? _____

- How will you measure its success? _____

PEOPLE

- Who is the character or characters? _____
  _____
  _____
  _____

- Where are they in their lives? _____
  _____
  _____
  _____

- What are they struggling with? _____
  _____
  _____
  _____

- What is their flawed belief about the world or themselves? _____
  _____
  _____
  _____

PROBLEM

- What happens that creates a new problem for them? _____
  _____
  _____
  _____

- Who or what comes along to help them? _____
  _____
  _____
  _____

- How do they finally accomplish their goal? _____
  _____
  _____
  _____

- How do they change as a result? _____
  _____
  _____
  _____

PURPOSE

- Who are you telling this story to? _____

- What is the emotion you want them to feel? _____

- What is the message you want them to receive? _____

- What action do you want your audience to take? _____

PLATFORM

- What format will you use to tell this story? _____

- On which platform will you distribute it? _____

- How can you creatively repurpose it? _____

- How will you measure its success? _____

PEOPLE

- Who is the character or characters? _____
  _____
  _____
  _____

- Where are they in their lives? _____
  _____
  _____
  _____

- What are they struggling with? _____
  _____
  _____
  _____

- What is their flawed belief about the world or themselves? _____
  _____
  _____
  _____

PROBLEM

- What happens that creates a new problem for them? _____
  _____
  _____
  _____

- Who or what comes along to help them? _____
  _____
  _____
  _____

- How do they finally accomplish their goal? _____
  _____
  _____
  _____

- How do they change as a result? _____
  _____
  _____

STORY TITLE:

PURPOSE

- Who are you telling this story to? _____
  _____
  _____
  _____

- What is the emotion you want them to feel? _____
  _____
  _____
  _____

- What is the message you want them to receive? _____
  _____
  _____
  _____

- What action do you want your audience to take? _____
  _____
  _____
  _____

PLATFORM

- What format will you use to tell this story? _____
  _____
  _____
  _____

- On which platform will you distribute it? _____
  _____
  _____
  _____

- How can you creatively repurpose it? _____
  _____
  _____
  _____

- How will you measure its success? _____
  _____
  _____
  _____

DATE:

PEOPLE

- Who is the character or characters? _____
  _____
  _____
  _____

- Where are they in their lives? _____
  _____
  _____
  _____

- What are they struggling with? _____
  _____
  _____
  _____

- What is their flawed belief about the world or themselves? _____
  _____
  _____
  _____

PROBLEM

- What happens that creates a new problem for them? _____
  _____
  _____
  _____

- Who or what comes along to help them? _____
  _____
  _____
  _____

- How do they finally accomplish their goal? _____
  _____
  _____
  _____

- How do they change as a result? _____
  _____
  _____
  _____

STORY TITLE:

PURPOSE

- Who are you telling this story to? _____

- What is the emotion you want them to feel? _____

- What is the message you want them to receive? _____

- What action do you want your audience to take? _____

PLATFORM

- What format will you use to tell this story? _____

- On which platform will you distribute it? _____

- How can you creatively repurpose it? _____

- How will you measure its success? _____

PEOPLE

- Who is the character or characters? _____
  _____
  _____
  _____

- Where are they in their lives? _____
  _____
  _____
  _____

- What are they struggling with? _____
  _____
  _____
  _____

- What is their flawed belief about the world or themselves? _____
  _____
  _____
  _____

PROBLEM

- What happens that creates a new problem for them? _____
  _____
  _____
  _____

- Who or what comes along to help them? _____
  _____
  _____
  _____

- How do they finally accomplish their goal? _____
  _____
  _____
  _____

- How do they change as a result? _____
  _____
  _____
  _____

STORY TITLE:

PURPOSE

- Who are you telling this story to? _____
  _____
  _____
  _____

- What is the emotion you want them to feel? _____
  _____
  _____
  _____

- What is the message you want them to receive? _____
  _____
  _____
  _____

- What action do you want your audience to take? _____
  _____
  _____
  _____

PLATFORM

- What format will you use to tell this story? _____
  _____
  _____
  _____

- On which platform will you distribute it? _____
  _____
  _____
  _____

- How can you creatively repurpose it? _____
  _____
  _____
  _____

- How will you measure its success? _____
  _____
  _____
  _____

DATE:

PEOPLE

- Who is the character or characters? _____
_____
_____
_____

- Where are they in their lives? _____
_____
_____
_____

- What are they struggling with? _____
_____
_____
_____

- What is their flawed belief about the world or themselves? _____
_____
_____
_____

PROBLEM

- What happens that creates a new problem for them? _____
_____
_____
_____

- Who or what comes along to help them? _____
_____
_____
_____

- How do they finally accomplish their goal? _____
_____
_____
_____

- How do they change as a result? _____
_____
_____
_____

STORY TITLE:

PURPOSE

- Who are you telling this story to? _____
_____
_____
_____

- What is the emotion you want them to feel? _____
_____
_____
_____

- What is the message you want them to receive? _____
_____
_____
_____

- What action do you want your audience to take? _____
_____
_____
_____

PLATFORM

- What format will you use to tell this story? _____
_____
_____
_____

- On which platform will you distribute it? _____
_____
_____
_____

- How can you creatively repurpose it? _____
_____
_____
_____

- How will you measure its success? _____
_____
_____
_____

DATE:

PEOPLE

- Who is the character or characters? _____
  _____
  _____
  _____

- Where are they in their lives? _____
  _____
  _____
  _____

- What are they struggling with? _____
  _____
  _____
  _____

- What is their flawed belief about the world or themselves? _____
  _____
  _____
  _____

PROBLEM

- What happens that creates a new problem for them? _____
  _____
  _____
  _____

- Who or what comes along to help them? _____
  _____
  _____
  _____

- How do they finally accomplish their goal? _____
  _____
  _____
  _____

- How do they change as a result? _____
  _____
  _____
  _____

STORY TITLE:

PURPOSE

- Who are you telling this story to? _____
  _____
  _____
  _____

- What is the emotion you want them to feel? _____
  _____
  _____
  _____

- What is the message you want them to receive? _____
  _____
  _____
  _____

- What action do you want your audience to take? _____
  _____
  _____
  _____

PLATFORM

- What format will you use to tell this story? _____
  _____
  _____
  _____

- On which platform will you distribute it? _____
  _____
  _____
  _____

- How can you creatively repurpose it? _____
  _____
  _____
  _____

- How will you measure its success? _____
  _____
  _____
  _____

PEOPLE

- Who is the character or characters? _____

- Where are they in their lives? _____

- What are they struggling with? _____

- What is their flawed belief about the world or themselves? _____

PROBLEM

- What happens that creates a new problem for them? _____

- Who or what comes along to help them? _____

- How do they finally accomplish their goal? _____

- How do they change as a result? _____

[STORY TITLE:

PURPOSE

- Who are you telling this story to? _____

- What is the emotion you want them to feel? _____

- What is the message you want them to receive? _____

- What action do you want your audience to take? _____

PLATFORM

- What format will you use to tell this story? _____

- On which platform will you distribute it? _____

- How can you creatively repurpose it? _____

- How will you measure its success? _____

PEOPLE

- Who is the character or characters? _____
  _____
  _____
  _____

- Where are they in their lives? _____
  _____
  _____
  _____

- What are they struggling with? _____
  _____
  _____
  _____

- What is their flawed belief about the world or themselves? _____
  _____
  _____
  _____

PROBLEM

- What happens that creates a new problem for them? _____
  _____
  _____
  _____

- Who or what comes along to help them? _____
  _____
  _____
  _____

- How do they finally accomplish their goal? _____
  _____
  _____
  _____

- How do they change as a result? _____
  _____
  _____
  _____

STORY TITLE:

PURPOSE

- Who are you telling this story to? _____
_____
_____
_____

- What is the emotion you want them to feel? _____
_____
_____
_____

- What is the message you want them to receive? _____
_____
_____
_____

- What action do you want your audience to take? _____
_____
_____
_____

PLATFORM

- What format will you use to tell this story? _____
_____
_____
_____

- On which platform will you distribute it? _____
_____
_____
_____

- How can you creatively repurpose it? _____
_____
_____
_____

- How will you measure its success? _____
_____
_____
_____

PEOPLE

- Who is the character or characters? _____

  _____

  _____

  _____

- Where are they in their lives? _____

  _____

  _____

  _____

- What are they struggling with? _____

  _____

  _____

  _____

- What is their flawed belief about the world or themselves? _____

  _____

  _____

  _____

PROBLEM

- What happens that creates a new problem for them? _____

  _____

  _____

  _____

- Who or what comes along to help them? _____

  _____

  _____

  _____

- How do they finally accomplish their goal? _____

  _____

  _____

  _____

- How do they change as a result? _____

  _____

  _____

  _____

STORY TITLE:

PURPOSE

- Who are you telling this story to? _____
_____
_____

- What is the emotion you want them to feel? _____
_____
_____

- What is the message you want them to receive? _____
_____
_____

- What action do you want your audience to take? _____
_____
_____

PLATFORM

- What format will you use to tell this story? _____
_____
_____

- On which platform will you distribute it? _____
_____
_____

- How can you creatively repurpose it? _____
_____
_____

- How will you measure its success? _____
_____
_____

PEOPLE

- Who is the character or characters? _____
  _____
  _____
  _____

- Where are they in their lives? _____
  _____
  _____
  _____

- What are they struggling with? _____
  _____
  _____
  _____

- What is their flawed belief about the world or themselves? _____
  _____
  _____
  _____

PROBLEM

- What happens that creates a new problem for them? _____
  _____
  _____
  _____

- Who or what comes along to help them? _____
  _____
  _____
  _____

- How do they finally accomplish their goal? _____
  _____
  _____
  _____

- How do they change as a result? _____
  _____
  _____
  _____

STORY TITLE:

PURPOSE

- Who are you telling this story to? _____
  _____
  _____

- What is the emotion you want them to feel? _____
  _____
  _____

- What is the message you want them to receive? _____
  _____
  _____

- What action do you want your audience to take? _____
  _____
  _____

PLATFORM

- What format will you use to tell this story? _____
  _____
  _____

- On which platform will you distribute it? _____
  _____
  _____

- How can you creatively repurpose it? _____
  _____
  _____

- How will you measure its success? _____
  _____
  _____

PEOPLE

- Who is the character or characters? _____
  _____
  _____
  _____

- Where are they in their lives? _____
  _____
  _____
  _____

- What are they struggling with? _____
  _____
  _____
  _____

- What is their flawed belief about the world or themselves? _____
  _____
  _____
  _____

PROBLEM

- What happens that creates a new problem for them? _____
  _____
  _____
  _____

- Who or what comes along to help them? _____
  _____
  _____
  _____

- How do they finally accomplish their goal? _____
  _____
  _____
  _____

- How do they change as a result? _____
  _____
  _____

[STORY TITLE:]

PURPOSE

• Who are you telling this story to? _____
_____
_____
_____

• What is the emotion you want them to feel? _____
_____
_____
_____

• What is the message you want them to receive? _____
_____
_____
_____

• What action do you want your audience to take? _____
_____
_____
_____

PLATFORM

• What format will you use to tell this story? _____
_____
_____
_____

• On which platform will you distribute it? _____
_____
_____
_____

• How can you creatively repurpose it? _____
_____
_____
_____

• How will you measure its success? _____
_____
_____
_____

DATE:

PEOPLE

- Who is the character or characters? _____
  _____
  _____

- Where are they in their lives? _____
  _____
  _____

- What are they struggling with? _____
  _____
  _____

- What is their flawed belief about the world or themselves? _____
  _____
  _____

PROBLEM

- What happens that creates a new problem for them? _____
  _____
  _____

- Who or what comes along to help them? _____
  _____
  _____

- How do they finally accomplish their goal? _____
  _____
  _____

- How do they change as a result? _____
  _____
  _____

STORY TITLE:

PURPOSE

- Who are you telling this story to? _____

_____

_____

- What is the emotion you want them to feel? _____

_____

_____

- What is the message you want them to receive? _____

_____

_____

- What action do you want your audience to take? _____

_____

_____

PLATFORM

- What format will you use to tell this story? _____

_____

_____

- On which platform will you distribute it? _____

_____

_____

- How can you creatively repurpose it? _____

_____

_____

- How will you measure its success? _____

_____

_____

DATE:

PEOPLE

- Who is the character or characters? _____
  _____
  _____
  _____

- Where are they in their lives? _____
  _____
  _____
  _____

- What are they struggling with? _____
  _____
  _____
  _____

- What is their flawed belief about the world or themselves? _____
  _____
  _____
  _____

PROBLEM

- What happens that creates a new problem for them? _____
  _____
  _____
  _____

- Who or what comes along to help them? _____
  _____
  _____
  _____

- How do they finally accomplish their goal? _____
  _____
  _____
  _____

- How do they change as a result? _____
  _____
  _____
  _____

[STORY TITLE:]

- Who are you telling this story to? _____
_____
_____
_____

- What is the emotion you want them to feel? _____
_____
_____
_____

- What is the message you want them to receive? _____
_____
_____
_____

- What action do you want your audience to take? _____
_____
_____
_____

[PLATFORM]

- What format will you use to tell this story? _____
_____
_____
_____

- On which platform will you distribute it? _____
_____
_____
_____

- How can you creatively repurpose it? _____
_____
_____
_____

- How will you measure its success? _____
_____
_____
_____

DATE:

PEOPLE

- Who is the character or characters? _____
_____
_____
_____

- Where are they in their lives? _____
_____
_____
_____

- What are they struggling with? _____
_____
_____
_____

- What is their flawed belief about the world or themselves? _____
_____
_____
_____

PROBLEM

- What happens that creates a new problem for them? _____
_____
_____
_____

- Who or what comes along to help them? _____
_____
_____
_____

- How do they finally accomplish their goal? _____
_____
_____
_____

- How do they change as a result? _____
_____
_____
_____

STORY TITLE:

PURPOSE

- Who are you telling this story to? _____
  _____
  _____
  _____

- What is the emotion you want them to feel? _____
  _____
  _____
  _____

- What is the message you want them to receive? _____
  _____
  _____
  _____

- What action do you want your audience to take? _____
  _____
  _____
  _____

PLATFORM

- What format will you use to tell this story? _____
  _____
  _____
  _____

- On which platform will you distribute it? _____
  _____
  _____
  _____

- How can you creatively repurpose it? _____
  _____
  _____
  _____

- How will you measure its success? _____
  _____
  _____
  _____

DATE:

PEOPLE

- Who is the character or characters? _____

_____

_____

- Where are they in their lives? _____

_____

_____

- What are they struggling with? _____

_____

_____

- What is their flawed belief about the world or themselves? _____

_____

_____

PROBLEM

- What happens that creates a new problem for them? _____

_____

_____

- Who or what comes along to help them? _____

_____

_____

- How do they finally accomplish their goal? _____

_____

_____

- How do they change as a result? _____

_____

_____

STORY TITLE:

PURPOSE

- Who are you telling this story to? _____
_____
_____
_____

- What is the emotion you want them to feel? _____
_____
_____
_____

- What is the message you want them to receive? _____
_____
_____
_____

- What action do you want your audience to take? _____
_____
_____
_____

PLATFORM

- What format will you use to tell this story? _____
_____
_____
_____

- On which platform will you distribute it? _____
_____
_____
_____

- How can you creatively repurpose it? _____
_____
_____
_____

- How will you measure its success? _____
_____
_____
_____

Made in the USA
Las Vegas, NV
22 November 2024

12404288R00115